Joseph Locke

An illustrated life of Joseph Locke

1805-1860

Charles Walker

Shire Publications Ltd.

Contents

ACKNOWLEDGEMENTS

Illustrations are acknowledged as follows: Radio Times Hulton Picture Library, pages 2, 7, 29, 34, 37; E. G. Tasker, pages 4, 44; Science Museum, South Kensington, pages 9 (top), 13 (bottom), and cover; Charles Walker, pages 9 (bottom), 13 (top), 21, 24; Railway Museum, York, page 14; British Transport Commission: Historical Relics Department, page 17; N. W. Webster (from his 'Joseph Locke — Railway Revolutionary'), page 43. The illustration on page 38 is from 'The Life of Robert Stephenson' by J. C. Jeaffreson (1864). The maps on pages 19 and 33 were drawn by R. G. Holmes.

Printed by C. I. Thomas & Sons (Haverfordwest) Ltd.

(Facing page) Joseph Locke in later life. One of the great triumvirate of railway engineers, with I. K. Brunel and Robert Stephenson, Locke is the least known of the three, yet also perhaps the greatest.

Joseph Locke

(Above) Joseph Locke was sent to the Grammar School in Church Street, Barnsley, where he remained until he was thirteen.

(Left) An 1873 poster announcing an examination for 'Locke Scholarships' to Barnsley Grammar School. Successful candidates were expected to study land surveying, mining and colliery engineering.

4

An unpromising boy

EARLY RAILWAY BUILDERS

Although George Stephenson was the father of modern railways, he built very few. His greatness lay in showing that railways could be built and that locomotives could operate them, and in proving it conclusively by constructing the Liverpool & Manchester Railway and its first engine, the *Rocket*. By then he was fifty years old, and that made him an old man in the early nineteenth century.

So the great railway systems of Britain and the world were laid down by others, especially his son and his old pupils. They, together with men like Brunel, built on his sound foundations and evolved the body of civil engineering theory and practice that his achievements and his advocacy made necessary.

Joseph Locke was unquestionably Stephenson's greatest pupil, in many respects greater than George's son Robert, but his genius was largely unrecognised in his lifetime and for a century after his death. One reason for this is that he did not have a competent biographer, such as Samuel Smiles who wrote about the two Stephensons. So records of Locke's work remained buried in the old railway companies' minute-books. Only recently have they been made accessible to historians who are now discovering how great he was.

Another reason was the lack of spectacular features in his work. He always aimed to build the shortest possible railway at the lowest possible cost, never constructing expensive bridges, viaducts and tunnels if he could avoid them. So his railways were financially sound and usually profitable, unlike many others which cost so much to build that their hopes of profitability were slight.

EARLY LIFE

There was little promise of future greatness in Locke's childhood. He was born on 9th August 1805, the son of William Locke who, like his father before him, spent his life in the coal-mining industry. A very able man of uncertain temper, William seldom stayed long in one place, and he and his wife, with their four sons and three daughters, were constantly moving to new homes. It was an unsettling life for children but it seems not to have affected the young Lockes.

The family moved to Barnsley when Joseph was five years old and, to give him a start in life, his father sent him to the grammar school there in due course. Although good at mathematics, he did not shine at school because, his sister said afterwards, he was mixed up with all the mischief going. But he could work quickly and well when he wished.

FIRST EMPLOYMENT

He left school in 1818, aged thirteen, and went to work as pupil of William Stobart, agent and colliery viewer to the Duke of Norfolk at Pelaw, Tyne and Wear. He stayed there for two years and left when he was expected to do menial work unconnected with the professional studies he was supposed to be making. Another pupillage, this time with a land surveyor at Rochdale, ended in a fortnight, for he discharged himself when he found that part of his duties consisted of minding the baby.

He returned home to a displeased father who gave him work as a clerk at the colliery he then managed. Joseph could do his clerical work quickly and easily, but when his spare time was to be occupied with more menial work like delivering coal he again became deeply dissatisfied. He toyed with the idea of emigrating to America.

But better times were coming. William Locke received a visit from his old friend George Stephenson, rapidly becoming famous as a builder of railways and locomotives. He was continually searching for bright young men to train as assistants, and finding that young Joseph seemed likely material, offered to take him as his pupil. The offer was accepted and in the summer of 1823, at the age of eighteen, he went to the Forth Street works of Robert Stephenson & Company, Newcastle upon Tyne. His terms of service were: his father to pay no premiums, Joseph to make himself generally useful, to learn all he could about railways and engines, and to receive no pay for three years.

(Facing page) Thomas Brassey (1805-1870) became the foremost railway contractor of the age. He worked with Locke on many projects, and Locke gave Brassey his first contract.

One result of this early training in the works was to make him a competent locomotive engineer. It gave him, too, an appreciation of the capabilities of locomotives, something which the two Stephensons did not possess. Realising this, he built railways with much steeper banks or gradients than his competitors, but in consequence much less costly, giving a better prospect of returns on the capital invested in them.

STEPHENSON'S ASSISTANT

Locke did not stay long in the works, for his master soon realised that he was a gifted pupil with a deep sense of responsibility who could be trusted with the most difficult tasks, but while there he and George's son Robert, who was of the same age, became very great friends. From then on he was, as Locke said when Robert died, 'the friend of my youth, the companion of my ripening years, and a competitor in the race of life'. Even a violent and life-long quarrel between Locke and Robert's father failed to break up the friendship.

He soon realised that his education was not good enough to enable him to become a successful engineer. Perhaps he regretted his wasted time at school. He made up for it by attending classes in mathematics, physics and mechanical drawing and, being a quick learner, soon became proficient in them.

He made such excellent progress that in two years Stephenson promoted him from being an unpaid pupil to a paid assistant at a salary of £80 a year. One of his first tasks was to take charge of building the Black Fell Colliery Railway, 6 miles long and complicated in design. How many youngsters, not twenty-one years old and after only two years as a pupil, could have done so well? That finished, he went off to survey for three more lines, the Leeds & Selby, the Manchester & Bolton, and the Canterbury & Whitstable. He supervised much of the building of the last named, and his extremely accurate engineering of the half-mile tunnel reinforced his excellent reputation.

This was a prelude to much more important work, the building of the Liverpool & Manchester Railway, in which he played a big part. George Stephenson, its chief engineer, divided the line into three sections, each under an assistant. Locke took charge of the western, Liverpool, section, so he was responsible for Olive Mount cutting and Wapping tunnel. The latter was very difficult and everyone concerned watched anxiously as the bores, driven in from each end and outwards

(Above) Olive Mount cutting at the western end of the Liverpool & Manchester Railway. This was on the section of the line for which Locke was responsible as assistant to George Stephenson.
(Below) Penkridge viaduct on the Grand Junction Railway in Staffordshire was Brassey's first railway contract. It was designed by Locke.

from seven or eight vertical shafts, approached each other. They met perfectly, and Locke's accurate work was noted approvingly by many businessmen who would be promoting more railways in the near future.

THE QUARREL

Unfortunately he quarrelled with his master soon afterwards. George Stephenson had consistently urged use of locomotives to haul the trains, but the railway's directors were recommended by two eminent engineers, James Walker and John Rastrick, to use twenty-one fixed engines spaced about 1½ miles apart, to pull the trains by means of cables wound round revolving drums. After doing a good deal of research, Locke and Robert Stephenson wrote a pamphlet showing that locomotive haulage would be faster, cheaper and more efficient. As chief engineer, George Stephenson demanded that his name should appear as author, but Locke, who actually wrote it, insisted that his name must appear on it. Finally, the two agreed very reluctantly that it should be headed 'compiled from the reports of Mr George Stephenson by Robert Stephenson and Joseph Locke, Civil Engineers'.

Locomotive haulage was adopted after a contest, the Rainhill Trials, in which Stephenson's *Rocket* beat three other contenders, but the quarrel continued. At the time, Locke had been sent by Stephenson to survey for the Manchester & Stockport Railway, leaving another assistant, Tom Gooch, to build the Edge Hill tunnel. Gooch made some surveying mistakes and the company directors asked Locke, whose accuracy they respected, to check. He found mistakes so great that the bores advancing from each end would never have met. As chief engineer, Stephenson should have checked, and when his shortcomings were exposed by his other assistant, Locke, he was angrier than ever. He decided to take Locke down a peg or two; in fact, his actions set Locke's feet even more firmly on the road to success.

However, Locke took charge of arrangements when the line was opened on 30th September 1830. Unfortunately the engine he was driving, *Rocket*, ran down and killed William Huskisson MP, powerful advocate of railways, deeply shocking Locke. But he continued to drive, two notable runs being made when he drove the French Emperor from London to Southampton whence, rough seas preventing embarkation, he drove him back to London.

The road to success

THE GRAND JUNCTION RAILWAY

Following the success of the Liverpool & Manchester Railway, George Stephenson's next great line was to run from Liverpool to Birmingham through Stafford and Wolverhampton. Locke carried out the survey and planned a line to run from Newton-le-Willows on the Liverpool & Manchester, giving access to both cities. The line, the Grand Junction, was sanctioned by Parliament on 6th May 1833, and everyone expected that Stephenson would appoint his brilliant young assistant, Locke, to take charge. But Stephenson had other ideas and appointed Locke resident engineer for a section near Birmingham only.

Neither Locke nor the directors would agree to this, and as Stephenson refused to reconsider it the directors overruled him and appointed Locke resident engineer for the section from near Crewe to Liverpool, adding that in Stephenson's absence he should be chief engineer for the whole. Stephenson swore never to be absent and appointed Rastrick resident engineer for the southern section near Birmingham.

LOCKE'S METHODS

Having already decided how to tackle the work, Locke began energetically. He drew exact plans of every yard of the line and every bridge, cutting and embankment, working out the cost of each part very accurately. Then he invited contractors to study his plans and give him tenders for completing stretches of ten miles, accepting those which were closest to his own estimates. The method was so successful that by 25th September 1834 contracts for the entire section had been placed.

Meanwhile, on the Birmingham section Rastrick, with Stephenson's concurrence, had prepared plans and specifications so imprecise that contractors, not clear on what was required, could not tender. Even by November only a few tenders had been received, and no contracts had been placed. Worried once more, the directors requested Locke to revise the specifications. Those for the Penkridge viaduct show what he discovered. On Rastrick's figures, Thomas Brassey had tendered at £26,000. After Locke's revision he altered his tender to £6,000, obtained the contract, and built the viaduct at a satisfactory profit.

The upshot was that in December Locke and George Stephenson were appointed joint engineers, but the arrangement proved unworkable, and in August 1835 Stephenson resigned, leaving Locke as chief engineer. So to him went the credit for building this very fine railway.

A NOTABLE SUCCESS

Locke's work on the Grand Junction, which took three years to build, was a model for all future railway builders, for he had learned the lessons of the Liverpool & Manchester. That line had cost nearly double its original estimate and had taken longer to build than expected because planning and specification were imprecise. Locke knew that railways could never be successful unless this waste was eliminated, since receipts could never pay adequate returns on such wasteful capital expenditure. He introduced a new system and proved its worth by building the Grand Junction at its estimated cost and to time. Opening should have been by the end of June 1837; the first passengers were carried on 4th July.

His experience on the earlier line had also warned him about contractors, for numbers of small men, some incompetent and some dishonest, had been used. On the Grand Junction he gave each contractor ten miles and, with an eye to the future, measured each man's performance against his promise. Only the efficient and successful need expect further work from him.

Another aspect of his planning was his refusal to countenance the unnecessarily spectacular. Every feature on the line had to be plain and functional, designed to do its job safely at the lowest cost. This was one of his guiding lights throughout his career and promoters of new railways turned to him gratefully. Most of them had had experience of flamboyant engineers who spent more on ornamenting a feature than on the feature itself. Castellated tunnels and bridges were not for him, and he would never have added the lions to Stephenson's Britannia Bridge. He even preferred difficult gradients to great earthworks, cuttings and tunnels, recognising the difference in cost.

(Above) Nantwich station on the Shrewsbury & Crewe Railway, built by Locke between 1853 and 1858, one of his later works.
(Below) Osborne's map of the Grand Junction Railway (1836). The line ran from Birmingham to Newton on the Liverpool & Manchester Railway.

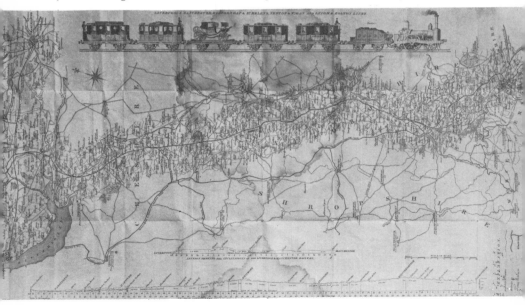

THE TOWN OF CREWE

When the Grand Junction was completed, Locke remained as its engineer until its amalgamation with the London & Birmingham to form the London & North Western in 1846, and he was engineer for the Grand Junction section of that line till 1849. During that time he carried out another great work on it, planning and building Crewe and its works.

The Grand Junction bought its first engines from specialist firms of engine builders, and they often proved unsatisfactory. Workshops were built at Edge Hill, Liverpool, to carry out necessary repairs, modifications and maintenance, but the volume of these grew so great that the small establishment there was quickly outgrown. With no room for expansion, a new site was sought and the choice fell on Crewe, half-way between the termini at Liverpool and Birmingham, and lying in open country. The spot had the added advantage that two railways to join the Grand Junction there had been sanctioned, the Manchester & Crewe and the Chester & Crewe.

So on 1st July 1840 the directors instructed Locke 'to prepare plans,

Columbine', completed on 20th February 1845, was the first locomotive constructed at Crewe and remained in service until 1902. The driving wheels are 6 feet 3 inches in diameter.

drawings and estimates for an establishment at Crewe; which shall include the shops required for the building and repair of carriages and wagons, as well as engines'. In spite of his involvement with much other work, Locke threw himself into the huge task so effectively that by early 1842 the works and two hundred cottages for the workers were under construction. By November 1842 he received further orders — 'to give minute and specific directions on details, fix wage rates, and personally superintend organisation of the new establishment to give the basis of an economical system for all time coming'. It would be impossible to provide more telling evidence of the fact that as a railway engineer he was an all-rounder, and also an economist of some ability.

In addition, he planned a church and school, built a gasworks, and supplied the new town with water. Further proof of his versatility is given by the completion on 20th February 1845 of Crewe's first engine, *Columbine*, which he helped to design, and which is now preserved at the railway museum at York. And the organisation he laid down was so good that by 1848 a new engine, complete with tender, was being completed each week.

LOCKE'S GREAT QUALITIES

Building the Grand Junction was Locke's first piece of unsupervised work, yet in its execution he proved himself to be a master, and it was the forerunner of many similar performances. What specific qualities did he bring to bear on these complex problems?

Unquestionably the first was his recognition of the need for method. His meticulous planning was the corner-stone of his success. This enabled him to make the realistic estimates that no other railway engineer of the time could achieve. His Grand Junction cost £18,500 per mile against his estimate of £17,000. Robert Stephenson's London & Birmingham cost £51,000 per mile; his estimate was £22,000. Rastrick's London & Brighton, estimated at £1,120,000 was unfinished after expenditure of £4,200,000 in money and four years in time. Brunel's estimate of £2,500,000 was £4,000,000 short of the actual cost of the Great Western. Locke's estimating was mastery indeed.

His devotion to method showed up in the allocation of contracts. He appointed proven and substantial contractors and supervised them closely. He gave them clear specifications and demanded from them a deposit of ten per cent of the contract price to prevent them sloping —

15

doing the easy parts of the contracts, collecting interim payments and then departing, leaving a mess. This was a sadly prevalent practice. He also made them provide their own tools and equipment, knowing that if the company provided them they would be smashed up very quickly.

THE LONDON & SOUTHAMPTON RAILWAY

While Locke was building the Grand Junction, Francis Giles planned and began building the London & Southampton. But Giles failed to appreciate the need for efficient planning and organisation, and very soon the work was in a state of chaos from which he had no hope of extricating it. In 1837 its directors persuaded him to resign and invited Locke, whose reputation on completion of the Grand Junction stood so high, to take his place.

Knowing that the offer would come, Locke had already diagnosed the ills, and he set about curing them energetically. He first tackled planning and specification and virtually replanned the line from its Nine Elms, London, terminus, through Weybridge, Basingstoke and Winchester to Southampton itself, specifying everything with his usual care. Turning to contractors, he found many small and inefficient muddlers working on tiny contracts. At this point a streak of ruthlessness showed up in his character. He eliminated all who showed no promise of ability to cope, gave ten-mile stretches to the more promising ones, and brought in Brassey to do the long hard section of cuttings and embankments through the chalk between Basingstoke and Winchester, giving him further contracts nearer London later.

Brassey, a Cheshire yeoman's son, owed his rise in the contracting world to Locke, whose patronage was shrewdly bestowed. He built lines for many other great engineers and at his peak had 100,000 men working for him, spread over five continents, his reputation being outstanding. Like Locke he was intensely energetic and the two often tramped the working sites together, covering great distances at speeds no other engineer or contractor could equal, and not glancing cursorily but seeing everything. They complemented each other. Locke designed Brassey's best work: Brassey executed Locke's best.

Locke's record on the Grand Junction shows his part in this. He would walk from Warrington to Birmingham in three days, almost killing his complaining assistants in the process. He invariably recognised difficulties which could cause delays in completion and took

Weybridge cutting on the London & Southampton Railway under construction. Locke took over as engineer of this line in 1837 and it was completed in 1840.

steps to overcome these as soon as they appeared.

So great was Locke's drive that the London & Southampton line was completed in 1840, and for nine years after that he held the arduous post of chief engineer, planning many lines for it. He built branches to Salisbury and to Gosport, the latter to serve Portsmouth. But the Gosport branch was one of his less successful pieces of work, for the clay embankments refused to stabilise, constant slipping prevented opening to time, and closure was necessary for a time after the first opening.

THE MANCHESTER & SHEFFIELD RAILWAY

Locke's rescue of the Southampton line still further enhanced his reputation, and when the Manchester & Sheffield fell into similar difficulties it was natural that he should be called in. He had some acquaintance with it already for both he and C. B. Vignoles had carried out surveys and produced almost identical plans. Although the commission to build went to Vignoles, some of the directors would have preferred Locke, and they helped to undermine Vignoles's position by constant criticism. There was some justification, for he was repeating the old mistakes of imprecise planning and specification, and using small, unreliable contractors. As a result confidence was lost and the sale of shares, on which building depended, almost stopped.

To help the company, Vignoles took up large blocks of shares and persuaded his friends to do the same, but as instalments of the price of these, known as calls, fell due, he was unable to meet them. He asked to be relieved of the obligation, and when the directors refused he resigned, leaving the way open for Locke to replace him in May 1839.

WOODHEAD TUNNEL

As before, Locke replaced the many small and unreliable contractors with men like Brassey, who built 19 miles, giving them the clear drawings and specifications previously lacking. Thanks to this, the line was opened from Manchester to Woodhead by August 1843 and from Sheffield to Woodhead by June 1845, leaving a three-mile gap at Woodhead itself, where an army of navvies was punching the summit tunnel through the Pennines.

The tunnel had brought nothing but trouble. Vignoles had costed it at £106,000, not providing for a brick lining as he thought that the rock was firm. Locke began by doubling the figure, realising that soft shales and water were present, necessitating both lining and continuous pumping. Boring was taking place from both ends and from five vertical shafts, and Vignoles had several small contractors working on the various faces. Locke replaced them by two only, Nicholson and Hattersley, noted for their brutally ruthless methods.

In spite of this, the single-line tunnel took six years to bore and involved excavating 250,000 tons of rock. During those years twenty-eight men were killed and over 650 injured; and when a parliamentary committee investigated, its members were told that stricter safety regulations would cost more in time and money. Since human lives were cheaper, the explanation was accepted. When the Government inspector examined it in December 1845, prior to its opening, he described it as one of the finest pieces of engineering he had ever seen. In 1847, with Locke again as engineer, a second bore was begun and it proved just as difficult, taking five years to build. The work on the Manchester & Sheffield still further strengthened Locke's reputation.

(Facing page) Map showing the principal railways engineered by Locke in Great Britain.

TO ABERDEEN

Forfar

SCOTTISH MIDLAND JUNCTION R. 1845-8

Perth

SCOTTISH CENTRAL R. 1845-8

STIRLING

CLYDESDALE JUNCTION R. 1845-8

Castlecary

Edinburgh

TO RUTHERGLEN

Motherwell

CARSTAIRS

CALEDONIAN R. 1837-48
(WORK BEGAN 1845)

BEATTOCK SUMMIT

Carlisle
1837-46

SHAP FELLS

1845-7

Windermere

Low Gill

Kendal

1856-61

OXENHOLME

Ingleton

Lancaster

1837-40

Preston

1839-45

Newton

Sheffield

GRAND JUNCTION R. 1831-7

TO LIVERPOOL

Manchester

Crewe

TO CHESTER

1853-8

TO STOKE & DERBY

Shrewsbury

STAFFORD

WOLVERHAMPTON

Norwich

TROWSE

1845-9

Haughley Junction

Birmingham

Bury St.Edmunds

1845-6

Ipswich

EASTERN UNION & HADLEIGH JUNCTION R. 1846-8

Hadleigh

BENTLEY

Colchester

1844-6

London

1837-40

BASINGSTOKE

Salisbury

Guildford

PORTSMOUTH DIRECT R. 1853-9

HONITON

South ampton

Exeter

Portsmouth

GOSPORT

SALISBURY & YEOVIL R. 1854-60

PARTNERS AND ASSISTANTS

The work already described, only a fraction of Locke's commitments in a very busy period of his life, was achieved because he had the ability to choose the right subordinates and was prepared to give them responsibility. Greatest of these was his partner John Edward Errington, who worked under Rastrick on the Birmingham section of the Grand Junction and who stayed on when Rastrick and George Stephenson resigned. Locke quickly found Errington to be hard-working, efficient and methodical and a man cast in his own mould. So the two became partners and worked together for more than twenty years, until Locke's death in 1860. He must share the credit for some of Locke's achievements.

A vice-president of the Institution of Civil Engineers at his death, Errington was a gifted engineer and not just Locke's junior partner. On many lines he surveyed, planned, piloted the bill through the parliamentary committee with great skill and supervised building, leaving little else to be done. He was an excellent bridge designer, being responsible for many on the Lancaster & Carlisle and Caledonian railways, as well as Thames bridges at Richmond, Kew and Kingston. Locke's lifelong friend and executor of his will, he helped his widow carry out many of Locke's wishes after his death.

Locke had numerous assistants, among whom were Alfred Jee, Peter Bruff and Sturges Meek. Jee did a good deal of work for him in Lancashire and Yorkshire, being a resident engineer on the Manchester & Sheffield, and doing much of the surveying and planning on the Huddersfield & Sheffield Junction. Bruff was resident engineer and did much of the work on Locke's three East Anglian lines, while Sturges Meek was in charge of the Liverpool, Ormskirk & Preston, among others. The use of these men takes nothing from the achievements of Locke. They demonstrated his ability to choose outstanding subordinates, and his willingness to trust them.

Locke also worked with some of the country's leading architects, the best known of whom, William Tite (later Sir William), was responsible for many of the station buildings on the London & Southampton Railway. On his East Anglian lines, Locke enlisted the services of local men, and their use of local materials and styles resulted in some very harmonious effects.

Haughley Junction station, Suffolk, where Locke's Ipswich & Bury and Haughley & Norwich lines met. The buildings are typical of many in East Anglia where Locke enlisted the help of local architects.

EVER NORTHWARD

Concurrently with the work already described, Locke was building a line in northern England and another in Scotland. In England, between 1830 and 1838, Vignoles had built somewhat inefficiently two railways, the Wigan Branch and the Preston & Wigan, amalgamated to form the North Union, connecting Newton-le-Willows, the northern point of the Grand Junction, with Preston. As Robert Stephenson's London & Birmingham was now open, there was a continuous line from London to Preston, 218½ miles. In 1836 Locke surveyed for a continuation to Lancaster, the Lancaster & Preston Junction, and began building it in 1837. The Grand Junction directors did not wish him to be too deeply involved, so Alfred Jee was appointed resident engineer.

Locke planned for the line to be built very economically, at a cost of £11,700 per mile, and one director boasted that it would be the cheapest railway ever built. But land costs shot up from an estimated £25,000 to £90,000, and when the Government insisted on bigger and stronger bridges the cost rose to £20,000. Even so, it was an inexpensive line, with no great cuttings, embankments and gradients, and its completion in 1840 pushed the railway frontiers forward by 21 miles.

21

LOCKE'S FIRST SCOTTISH LINE

Locke and Errington planned the Glasgow, Paisley & Greenock Railway and completed the first easy section to Paisley in July 1840. The section from Paisley to Greenock was more difficult, the hardest part consisting of two tunnels totalling 680 yards and 6 miles of cuttings through Bishopton Ridge. The rock was whinstone, so hard that in places a thousand men could only progress 6 inches in a day, in spite of the use of so much gunpowder that, says a contemporary report, the onlooker would have thought he was in the neighbourhood of a battle. Locke's ability to estimate was shown by the cost of this great excavation — £300 more than his figure of £85,000. Few engineers before or since could produce such figures.

When the line was opened in March 1841 with great ceremony and a costly banquet, its chairman introduced the name of Locke as 'not the property of this country only, but of Europe, which in all time coming would be associated with the history of locomotion by steam'. For Locke was also building the first great trunk line in France at the time.

While building the railway to Greenock, Locke and Errington were also rebuilding the harbour there. Much of the engineering was done by Errington, and Brassey was the contractor, as he was for the railway. The new harbour could accommodate five hundred ships with a draught up to 20 feet, and was a substantial contributor to the success of the line.

OTHER INTERESTS

In 1834, at the age of twenty-nine and just as he was becoming most deeply involved in building the Grand Junction Railway, he married Phoebe McCreery, daughter of a Liverpool printer and minor poet. His somewhat advanced age can be explained in two ways. He had had very little time for the social relaxation likely to bring him in contact with eligible ladies, and he had very little money. As Stephenson's assistant he received £100 a year. In 1833, when he became engineer for the northern section of the Grand Junction, his salary rose to £800, increasing in following years to £1,200 and £2,000. By then he could provide for a wife.

We know little enough about her, apart from the fact that she was a confirmed invalid who led a secluded life and was not expected to reach old age. In fact, she outlived her husband by six years. They had no children, but adopted a little girl whom they named Minna, and she was a source of joy to both of them, but especially to Phoebe, much of whose life must have been lonely, due to Locke's absences on professional work and parliamentary duties.

Their only home was at 26 Lowndes Square, London, near to their friends the Brasseys, and there is no record of Phoebe visiting Honiton, which had no residence, and which Locke bought solely to give him a parliamentary seat. Neither did she accompany him to Moffat for the masculine pursuit of grouse shooting.

In 1838 Locke was honoured by Fellowship of the Royal Society. His proposers included Rastrick, Sir John Rennie, Dr Dionysius Lardner and Sir Marc Brunel. They described him as 'Member of the Institution of Civil Engineers, Constructor of the Liverpool & Birmingham Railway and other great public works, and a Gentleman well conversant with every Department of practical Science'. He does not seem to have taken any active part in the Society's proceedings and did not present any papers.

He became a member of the Institution of Civil Engineers in 1830 and later took a very active part in its work, becoming a member of its council, vice-president and, in 1858-9, president. The subject of his presidential address was characteristic of him but unusual for an engineer. He spoke on the economics of railway building, comparing unfavourably those in Britain with those in France.

He explained that the French government laid down where railways could be built, made grants and low-interest loans, and guaranteed investors' interest. In Britain the Government only passed the act of authorisation. Large and small investors and the banking and financial houses provided the money speculatively and the entire process was haphazard. Difficulties were intensified by Parliament's hatred of monopolies, which caused it to sanction competing lines which could only damage each other. As a result, British lines cost £10,000 per mile more to build than did French lines.

The West Coast route

HIS GREATEST WORK

Locke's greatest work was unquestionably the construction of the trunk line from Lancaster through Carlisle to Glasgow, Edinburgh, Stirling, Perth and beyond. We have seen how he built the Grand Junction and the Lancaster & Preston Junction railways. At the same time he was deeply involved in the preliminaries for building northwards from Lancaster, a task in which he was backed by the directors of the Grand Junction.

As early as 1835 they instructed him to inspect possible routes from Lancaster to Carlisle, later to survey also between Carlisle and Glasgow. Their interest lay in their hope that the Grand Junction would become a part of a through route from London via the Midlands to Scotland, on which a vast amount of profitable traffic would be funnelled. In January 1836 Locke reported that a line to Glasgow could be built and, although several years were to pass before this dream became a reality, the directors were committed to it from then on.

TWO ROUTES TO CARLISLE

Characteristically Locke looked for the shortest way to Carlisle and found it to be through the mountains of Westmorland. So he planned a line leaving the Lancaster & Preston Junction south of Lancaster, which would be left on a short branch, missing Kendal, passing over Shap Fells, nearly 1,000 feet above sea level, and falling through Bampton and Penrith to Carlisle. It would pass through wild country and would be difficult to build, needing huge embankments, cuttings, viaducts and, as originally planned, a tunnel under Shap Fells. The heavy gradients would also make it difficult to work. But Locke

Shap Fells, 1,000 feet above sea level and typical of the remote country through which Locke built the Lancaster & Carlisle Railway. The smoke of the banking engine at the rear, necessary because of the gradient, can be seen in this pre-electrification photograph.

25

realised that a route further east would be through wilder country, while one far enough west would greatly increase the distance. His proposals were not universally popular: Lancaster citizens objected to being on a branch, Kendal inhabitants were displeased at being missed altogether, and the greatest landowner, Lord Lonsdale, disliked the route through the Lowther Valley.

George Stephenson favoured a coastal route. Unworried by its greater mileage, 25 miles longer, he preferred it to the heavy engineering of Locke's route, so he planned a line known as the Grand Caledonian Junction Railway, leaving Lancaster, crossing Morecambe Bay on a long embankment and following the coast through Whitehaven, Workington and Maryport. The cost of the embankment was to be defrayed by selling the land behind it reclaimed from the sea.

STEPHENSON VERSUS LOCKE AGAIN

The two schemes caused bitter controversy, Stephenson pouring scorn on Locke's and saying that since the line would pass through sparsely populated country its only passengers would be crows, and that ice and snow on the rails would stop trains from running over the fells throughout the winter. Locke said little, contenting himself with repeating that the trunk line to Scotland must follow the most direct route.

The controversy raged for several years, and modifications to both schemes were suggested. Locke's line might be altered to pass through Kendal, involving a tunnel 1,140 feet deep under Gatescarth Pass. It would have been very costly, and Locke would not consider it. He did agree to the main line route being altered to pass through Lancaster, at the cost of a large viaduct over the river Lune. Stephenson's line could be moved further south into Morecambe Bay, giving an even bigger embankment and more reclaimed land to sell.

The whole scheme was complicated by the activities of George Hudson, the Railway King, who was planning to build from York to Newcastle, as a stepping stone for a further leap to Berwick and Edinburgh. As it was currently believed that one line only could be built between England and Scotland, Hudson's work, over easier country, was an obvious threat to the West Coast schemes.

Hudson was a York draper who invested an inheritance of £30,000 in railways and was clever enough to go on and eventually obtain autocratic control of the Eastern Counties and the lines that made up the Midland and the North Eastern railways. The title of 'Railway King' came from the power he wielded, but later discovery of dishonest practices led to his disgrace and poverty-stricken exile in France.

THE ROYAL COMMISSION

At this stage the Government appointed a royal commission to advise on routes to Scotland, and this involved considering Locke's and Stephenson's plans, as well as Hudson's, together with the best route forward over the border, either from Carlisle or Berwick. Locke had already chosen a route from Carlisle, a direct but difficult one over Beattock Summit, 1,300 feet above sea level, in preference to a longer but flatter one nearer the west coast. Having considered all these plans, the commission accepted Locke's two direct routes on economic grounds, also preferring the Beattock or Annandale route, as it was called, as it led to both Glasgow and Edinburgh. But it also praised Hudson's East Coast route and suggested that when Newcastle was reached the Government should help to finance the remainder.

The last suggestion, made in March 1841, stirred the West Coast party into fierce activity. Meetings were held, and after much difficulty the money to build to Carlisle, £1,200,000, was promised by November 1843. Further north, many Scots showed little enthusiasm until the name of the proposed line from Carlisle to Glasgow and Edinburgh was announced as the Caledonian Railway. They could identify with this, and the money needed was promised.

THE LANCASTER & CARLISLE RAILWAY

By early 1844 Locke had finalised the plans and a bill was presented to Parliament. So sure of its success were the promoters that materials were ordered and the contract signed even before Parliament's authorisation, obtained on 24th May. Brassey and Mackenzie had tendered for the contract, as well as the successful and well-known contractor John Stephenson, no relation of George and Robert, and since their prices were almost identical they were persuaded to work together to increase speed. By now, Hudson's men were seventy miles north of York and working fast, and many observers thought that with this lead they could not be overtaken.

But the line proved to be one of the fastest and finest pieces of railway building ever carried out. This was the result of magnificent teamwork — meticulous planning by Locke and Errington and their resident engineers, Larmer and Worthington, and incredibly efficient organisation by Brassey, Mackenzie and John Stephenson, backed up by the efforts of a superb labour force. Work started a month after the act was passed, and, despite working under appalling conditions due to the heavy rainfall and to the material to be excavated, which varied from hardest rock to bottomless bog, it was completed in 29 months.

Reading contemporary accounts, we can only marvel. Much of the line ran through isolated country and there were no lodgings for the navvies, so they had to live in turf huts housing twenty or thirty men in misery and squalor. They rioted and terrorised the local inhabitants, and a committee appointed by Parliament said that they were more like animals than men.

Today we may find it difficult to appreciate the magnitude of their performance. But when we compare it with modern achievements we have to remember that the work was done almost entirely by human muscles, with no mechanisation; the only explosive was gunpowder; there were no telephones, no two-way radio sets, the poorest of communications with the working sites, no typewriters and no photocopiers for duplication of plans. Every drawing and letter was done by hand and every instruction given by hand-written letter or verbally. Even the men in charge, Locke Errington, Brassey, must often have been a long way from human ken as far as the men on the sites were concerned, for they were deeply occupied in many other schemes.

It was a remarkable achievement for which Locke must take the credit. Yet it was but a fraction of his total commitments. At the same time he was building three substantial lines in East Anglia, four in Scotland, and an important trunk line of great difficulty in France, as well as acting as chief engineer to the London & South Western, as the London & Southampton was now named, and to the Grand Junction. In addition, in the Lake District itself, he built the Kendal & Windermere, by means of which Kendal obtained its own railway. It ran from the main Lancaster & Carlisle at Oxenholme to Kendal, two miles away, and then to Birthwaite, not far from the present town of Windermere. Low Wood, a beauty spot on the shores of Windermere, was first proposed as terminus, but the opposition of the Lake Poets, led by Wordsworth, caused the change.

28

Four features on the Lancaster & Carlisle Railway: (top) Lowther viaduct; (above) Lancaster station; (right) Newbiggin bridge; (below) Eamont viaduct.

THE CALEDONIAN RAILWAY

The Caledonian, 122 miles long and costing £2,800,000, languished until the Lancaster & Carlisle got under way. Then, its role in the great north-south route becoming apparent, came action. The same team was in operation, Locke and Errington as engineers and Brassey, Mackenzie and Stephenson as contractors, and their performance was comparable with that on the southern line. There were many parallels between the two — isolated country, a great climb in the mountains, and every difficult type of soil and rock. The line climbed to 1,016 feet over Beattock Summit and at Carstairs forked, one branch going to Glasgow and one to Edinburgh. Two and a half years after the starting date the line was opened to both cities, on 15th February 1848. By now, the East Coast route, that deadly rival, was also open, apart from two gaps where it crossed the Tyne at Newcastle and the Tweed at Berwick.

THE RAILWAY MANIA

All this work is made more outstanding by being done during and immediately after the 'railway mania', when men, materials and money were becoming progressively scarcer. But in these cases money and materials were forthcoming because investors favoured Locke's lines, knowing that they would be well and economically built, and men could always be found by Brassey, whose reputation as a model employer stood him in good stead.

The 'railway mania' was an astonishing phenomenon in which people of all walks of life rushed to buy the shares of railways existing, projected and often mythical. In the years 1844-6 Parliament sanctioned building of 8,000 miles at an estimated cost of £210,000,000, more than the kingdom's annual income, and neither money, credit, proven contractors, manpower nor credible engineers existed to carry it out. When the bubble burst thousands of investors were ruined and many engineers, contractors and promoters were discredited. Locke's reputation and good sense enabled him to avoid the dubious and he was unscathed by it.

Railways overseas

TRUNK LINE IN FRANCE

The French were late in starting to build railways and when, noting the success of those built in Britain, they realised that railways must come, they turned to Britain for help, both financial and technical. Prospects for a line running westwards from Paris to Rouen and Le Havre were excellent, for there was already a large volume of passengers and goods travelling that route by road or down the Seine, neither very speedy. Le Havre was connected with Southampton, now itself a railway terminus, by means of a fast boat service, and there was little doubt that a faster railway journey would increase traffic considerably.

So in 1838 a group of French financiers sent Charles Lafitte, partner in a Paris banking firm, to urge the directors of the London & Southampton Railway to join them in building a railway from Paris to Rouen, with an extension later to Le Havre. Lafitte explained that French investors were less ready to support such schemes than were British, and he spoke so persuasively that Locke was sent to France to look over the route, accompanied by William Chaplin and William Reed, chairman and secretary of the company, to investigate commercial prospects.

They returned with a glowing report. Locke said that a line could be built cheaply. The eighty miles to Rouen would follow the Seine valley and would need no spectacular bridges, no big embankments and gradients, and one easy tunnel. Traffic prospects were equally good, and the London & Southampton directors agreed to support it.

FINANCING THE LINE

The French government was very helpful, lending 14,000,000 francs (£560,000) at low interest rates, leaving 36,000,000 francs (£1,440,000) to be raised. Half of this came from Britain and half from France,

Locke himself investing £10,000, a measure of his growing prosperity. The law authorising construction was passed in June 1839 and planning could begin. The French had no experienced railway engineers and they agreed to Locke's appointment as chief engineer. Once more, despite all other commitments, he threw himself into the work and did the planning with his usual care and attention to detail.

Neither had the French any experienced contractors, and Locke invited certain British contractors to tender. Among them, Brassey and his former rival, William Mackenzie, produced almost identical figures and they were persuaded to amalgamate and work jointly. They found little to trouble them on the contract, for the work was straightforward, and pushing on with incredible speed they finished well within the three years expected. Their greatest trouble was caused by the bad winter of 1843 which interrupted work for several weeks. To feed his navvies, shipped from England, and to keep them from leaving the sites and returning home, Brassey established soup kitchens and fed them. In consequence, the contract was completed by the end of April. At a grand ceremony the line was opened on 3rd May 1843 by the Duke of Nemours, son of the French king, Louis Philippe, Locke being highly praised and invested with the Cross of the Legion of Honour.

THE LOCOMOTIVE WORKS

During building of the line, Locke gave much thought to the question of locomotives and stock, and as France was as yet not building any he helped to establish the great works at Sotteville, near Rouen. He persuaded William Buddicom, who was then in charge of the Grand Junction works, to take it over and within a short time engines, carriages and trucks were being built, not only for the Paris & Rouen but also for many other lines under construction in France. In this connection, Locke's attention to detail is shown in the appointment of engine-drivers. Men could apply to the London or Paris offices of the company and, said an advertisement, Locke would personally interview them and they would have to satisfy him that they were competent.

ON TO LE HAVRE

Extension to Le Havre, planning for which began before the line to Rouen was completed, was much more difficult. Only 56 miles long, it had to start from the Rouen terminus, cross the Seine on a large

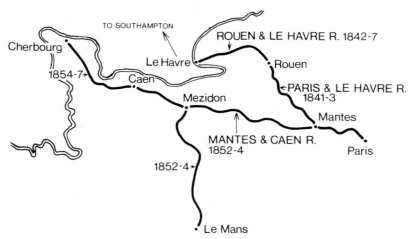

Map showing the principal railways constructed by Locke in France.

viaduct, tunnel under Rouen itself in three places, climb to 600 feet and return to sea level. Deep valleys crossed its route and these could only be crossed by viaducts, including four large ones at Darnetal, Mallaunay, Barentin and Bolbec. Though costs would be high, the French government helped by granting 8,000,000 francs (£320,000) and lending 10,000,000 francs (£400,000) at the low interest of three per cent. Even before authorisation, it was agreed that Locke should be engineer and Brassey and Mackenzie contractors again.

The government engineer suggested a route which Locke roughly followed, deviating only to miss the centres of towns and avoid costly gradients. Locke wished for maximum gradients of 1 in 110, but the inspector refused to permit any greater than 1 in 200. After Locke had produced figures relating to haulage of trains on gradients, a compromise of 1 in 125 was accepted, but even this annoyed Locke since it increased costs. As finally planned, the main features were the three Rouen tunnels totalling 3,200 metres, and the great viaducts previously mentioned. It was one of Locke's most spectacular and costly lines.

VIADUCT COLLAPSE

Apart from engineering difficulty, it was also a troublesome line, and at times must have worried Locke. He was in continual dispute with the government inspector over gradients, and he quarrelled with the inhabitants of towns about where the line should run. When it approached a town centre they grumbled because property had to be demolished. At Bolbec they grumbled because he avoided the town, which could only be reached by unacceptable gradients. So much fuss was made that he had to build a very steep horse-operated branch into the town.

The fall of the Barentin viaduct eclipsed all other troubles. Spanning a stream and crossing a valley there, Brassey built to Locke's designs a magnificent viaduct, 100 feet high with twenty-seven arches each spanning 50 feet. The last arches to be erected, the fourth and fifth from the Rouen end, were completed in November 1847, and ballasting ready for track-laying began early in January. At 6 a.m. on 10th January a boy fetching cattle from the fields heard bricks falling and

The opening of the Rouen & Le Havre Railway was marked by the blessing of locomotives and track by clergy.

looking up saw the fifth arch collapsing. Within two minutes the other twenty-six had fallen into a mass of rubble with a roar audible three miles away.

There was an immediate investigation and Locke's own report, only recently re-examined after a century of obscurity, blamed the standard of Brassey's masonry. Brassey's biographer attributed the cause to use of unsuitable local lime, against which Brassey had protested, for the mortar. Other accounts said that ballasting had begun before the mortar had set. Whatever the cause, Brassey's action was characteristic. Ignoring all recrimination, he rebuilt the viaduct at his own expense, using lime of his own choosing.

Rebuilding at a cost of between £30,000 and £50,000 was done so quickly that there was no delay in opening the line. But the government engineer, clearly doubtful of Locke's designs, insisted on strengthening other viaducts, and before he would sanction the line's opening he gathered together every engine he could find and lined them all up on each viaduct in turn. This so infuriated Locke that at the inaugural banquet he asserted that the inspector had deliberately tried to destroy them. Reading contemporary reports over a century later, the feeling that Locke's designs were not above suspicion and that Brassey was the scapegoat lingers strongly.

LATER FRENCH RAILWAYS

Despite the Barentin disaster, Locke enjoyed a tremendous reputation in France, and he might have gone on to build many more lines there. But in 1848 a revolution swept away Louis Philippe and replaced him by Louis Napoleon, whose new and intensely nationalistic government would not permit use of British engineers, capital and labour to build more French railways. Indeed, mobs were allowed to attack installations on the Paris & Le Havre Railway, including four Seine bridges, Paris, Batignolles and Rouen stations, and the Sotteville works, doing much damage, while the government itself threatened to confiscate the system, almost without compensation. The rulers had second thoughts, but for some years France was barred to British railway builders.

Locke and Brassey were recalled when Louis Napoleon, having completed Louis XIV's grand scheme for an arsenal and dockyard at Cherbourg, wanted it linked by rail with Paris. So in 1852 Locke returned to plan the line in two parts which had much in common with those of the earlier line. Leaving the Paris & Rouen at Mantes, a first section, 113 miles long, was built with little difficulty to Caen. His nephew, William Locke, and the Frenchman Neumann were his assistants, and two years sufficed for the work. The second part, from Caen to Cherbourg, also took two years but it was much more difficult. When the entire line was opened at a great ceremony at Cherbourg, Louis Napoleon awarded Locke and Brassey Crosses of the Legion of Honour. While building these lines the two were also engaged on the Le Mans and Mezidon Railway, 84 miles long.

LOCKE'S ACCIDENT

However, during this second spell in France Locke was involved in a severe accident. On 2nd November 1855, while he, his nephew and Brassey were inspecting the brickwork of a tunnel on the Mantes & Caen Railway, the scaffolding collapsed and let them fall some 12 feet. William Locke and Brassey were unhurt, but a beam fell across Joseph Locke's leg, causing a double fracture. Doctors wished to amputate, but Locke refused to agree, so he was taken to Paris, where other French doctors also recommended amputation. Refusing again, Locke sent for Sir Joseph Joliffe, British Embassy doctor, whose prescription of rest and cold water compresses proved successful. However, he suffered much pain and had a limp for the rest of his life, and it was noted that one effect was to age him considerably.

THE DUTCH RHENISH RAILWAY

Although all Locke's work cannot be included in a short account of his life, the Dutch Rhenish Railway may be described as one of his less satisfactory pieces of work. As planned, the line was to run from Amsterdam to Rotterdam via Utrecht, whence a branch would run to Arnhem and Emmerich, a total of 100 miles. Work began without British help, but when money ran out British investors were invited to participate, and on their insistence Locke was appointed engineer. In 1846 he inspected the work already done and was well impressed. He said that the remainder would be cheap and easy to build, thanks to the flatness of the country. His only doubt concerned the broad gauge of 1.95 metres (6 feet 9 inches) which differed from that of its neighbours,

A typically Dutch scene showing the Dutch Rhenish Railway crossing the Zyde-Plaa polder near Rotterdam.

necessitating costly trans-shipment of passengers and goods at the meeting points.

After that, years passed with little progress. The British shareholders held meetings at which they tried to speed up construction, and in 1851 Locke was asked to give the scheme more attention. He did so, revising the plans and again recommending change of gauge. But progress

37

remained slow, and quarrels between the Dutch engineers and Brassey's agent, Stephen Ballard, in which Locke was appointed arbitrator, did little to help. The gauge was changed in 1854 and the line was completed in 1857. Locke's work on this was below his usual standard although, to be fair to him, we cannot be sure whether he was engineer or consulting engineer. If the latter, that might provide an excuse.

Robert Stephenson in middle age. His father, George, took on Locke as a pupil, and the two young men became friends and remained so despite the quarrel between George and Locke.

A great man

LOCKE THE WORKER

After the quarrel with George Stephenson, Locke worked independently and in partnership with Errington for twenty-five years until his death in 1860, but for the last six he was doing less than in earlier years. Most of the work already described was carried out in less than twenty years, during which he was desperately busy. For the foregoing does not represent his total output by any means. In addition, he built three substantial lines in East Anglia, others in Scotland, branches for the London & South Western, quite a large mileage in Lancashire and the Barcelona & Mataro in Spain. He also did much work in planning lines which were never built due to the collapse of the 'railway mania'. He completely reconstructed the London & Blackwall, originally built to odd gauge and worked by stationary engines. His work enabled it in due course to fit neatly into the London, Tilbury & Southend, built later by G. P. Bidder.

THE PROFESSIONAL ENGINEER

The virtual ignoring of Locke since his death is most surprising in view of his high standing in his lifetime, a standing recognised by the press which classed him as one of the great triumvirate of railway engineers, the others being Robert Stephenson and Brunel. Such standing meant that he was in continual demand as an adviser to companies and as an expert witness to Government committees inquiring into the railway questions of the day.

His advice to the companies concerned such technical matters as types of sleepers and their preservation, rail and trackbed. He was often called in to give an independent opinion when difficulties arose—on, for instance, a series of derailments on the Crewe & Chester Railway, which he found to be due to a slightly odd gauge, and the exceeding of estimates by Colonel Landmann, engineer of the Preston

& Wyre, which Locke found to be justified. In the absence of relevant accounts we cannot tell how profitable such work was, but it must have taken up much of his time.

A most important body before which he testified was the Government's Gauge Commission of 1845. Exceptions to standard gauge were Brunel's Great Western of 7 feet and Braithwaite's Eastern Counties of 5 feet. Most professional opinion, as voiced by Locke, Robert Stephenson, Rastrick, Vignoles and others was that standard gauge should be compulsory. Brunel and the Great Western party, in particular, in opposing this, ignored the economics of trans-shipment where break of gauge occurred. The commission recommended that no more broad gauge should be laid, but more was built, notably on the Oxford, Worcester & Wolverhampton, laid to mixed gauge and a source of annoyance to Locke.

He also advised a parliamentary committee against adoption of the atmospheric principle of propulsion, opposing men like Brunel, Vignoles and Cubitt. The committee, wrongly as later events proved, reported in favour of the system. In general, Locke's logical and common-sense approach to such questions usually gave him the right answers.

THE MEMBER FOR HONITON

In December 1846 Locke bought the Manor of Honiton for £80,000, and his steward there immediately announced that he would be a candidate for the borough at the next parliamentary election. Honiton was one of the rotten boroughs, its three hundred electors being allowed to return two members. Locke was returned a year later and held the seat until his death. In politics he was a Liberal, but in his address he demanded civil and religious liberty, extension of the franchise, retrenchment in public expenditure and reform of obsolete institutions.

In practice he was noted for his independent outlook, and so he was never a safe party man. Characteristically, he studied every question carefully, brought to bear on it his personal brand of logic and common sense and formed his own judgements, in the light of which he then spoke and voted. In consequence, he was prepared to support Conservative reform bills which would have removed, among the rotten boroughs, his own seat. He spoke on the subjects he understood. Many

Scottish railways closed down from midnight on Saturdays, to midnight on Sundays, thus obeying literally the injunction against working on the sabbath. Even when, on Government orders, mail trains were run, carrying passengers was prohibited. Locke tried hard to get this changed without success.

PARLIAMENTARY CAMPAIGNS

He campaigned long for changes in the laws relating to the financing and accounting of railways, a field in which reform was badly needed, but again in vain. In his fight he was opposed by the companies themselves, for they particularly disliked one provision in a bill he introduced in 1851, for external auditing and publication of every railway company's accounts, and by the railway press, always subservient to the whims and fancies of certain shareholders. This campaign cost him much in popularity, but the measures he advocated were logical and in due course had to come.

In an interview with the *Railway Times* he gave his views on railway finances. He thought that accounts should be audited and on them should be based periodic revision of fares, that existing lines should be amalgamated for greater economy, that capital accounts, source of so much sharp practice, should be closed when a railway was completed, and that the overriding aim of the companies should be to further the public advantage. Nearly a century had to pass before some of the far-sighted reforms he advocated were adopted.

OTHER PARLIAMENTARY INTERESTS

His other parliamentary interests were estimates and ordnance surveys. He was, by practice, an authority on surveying, and both he and Robert Stephenson, member for Whitby, attacked a scheme for a very costly survey on the 25-inch scale then being carried out, pointing out that on so large a scale many constantly changing features would appear, so that maps would never be completely up-to-date and accurate. But the advice of the two men in the House of Commons with most practical experience was disregarded.

His attention to estimates also made him unpopular, for he attacked waste and bad practice wherever he found it, and departmental heads whose mistakes he exposed disliked him for it. In consequence, when Sir Benjamin Hall relinquished the position of Commissioner of Public

Works, and Locke's friends recommended him as the ideal candidate, the Government ignored him and appointed someone else. His friends suggested that he knew too much about public works to be given control over them, but his independence of mind and consequent unpopularity were the real reasons. His failure to obtain this post disappointed him very greatly.

THE MAN

Although his biographer of 1861, Joseph Devey, described Locke as a pleasant, genial and clubbable man with no defects, this is at variance with the facts as ascertained from other accounts, and especially from his own letters. Undoubtedly he could be utterly ruthless, but every successful railway engineer shared this trait, and to pretend that Locke lacked it is to see him unrealistically. It showed most in his dealings with contractors and in his behaviour towards people and companies with whom he quarrelled. On occasion his ruthlessness went so far as to approach viciousness.

Like all the northern school of engineers, he had an eye on the main chance and would accept any commission likely to bring him money. At times, too, this went beyond accepted limits. An excellent example, never previously quoted, concerns the building of a roof over Lime Street station, Liverpool. As chief engineer to that section of the London & North Western Railway he had considerable say in the choice of design, and when William Turner, a Dublin contractor, came up with a very novel design for a single-span roof Locke did all he could to discredit Turner with the directors, so that he could modify the design and use it himself. When the directors insisted on accepting Turner's design and gave him the contract to build, Locke, on the evidence of his own letters, did all he could to make things difficult.

LOCKE'S DEATH

For the last few years of his life Locke's main relaxation was grouse shooting on the moor he rented at Moffat, Dumfries-shire, and it was while there that he died suddenly on 18th September 1860. He had been in excellent spirits on Sunday 16th September, when no shooting was permitted, but he woke on Monday morning with severe abdominal pains which worsened as the day passed, and which the doctors summoned could not alleviate. The symptoms read like those

The tomb of Joseph Locke in Kensal Green Cemetery, London.

of appendicitis. After a night of great pain he died at eight o'clock on
the Tuesday morning.

His body was taken over the lines he had built — Caledonian,
Lancaster & Carlisle, Lancaster & Preston Junction and Grand
Junction — to London for burial in Kensal Green Cemetery. A window,
since removed, was dedicated to him in Westminster Abbey, but
permission for a statue by the Italian sculptor Marochetti who had
recently executed those of Brunel and Robert Stephenson,
commissioned by the Institution of Civil Engineers, to be placed at
Westminster, was refused by the Government, which still remembered
his independence. So the statue was erected in Locke Park, Barnsley,

presented to the town by his widow soon after his death. He died largely unhonoured and unsung, and that neglect has persisted for over a century.

LOCKE'S GREATNESS

His greatness stems partly from his appreciation that to be successful railways must be built on sound economic principles. When he began working, the trend was towards costly flamboyance. His insistence on economy — described by his rivals, he admitted, as 'slopwork' — made him uniquely great. Add to that the magnificent lines he built, described briefly in the foregoing pages, and we can only conclude that he was indeed a giant among railway engineers.

This statue of Locke, by Baron Marochetti, stands in Locke Park, Barnsley. It was presented to the town where he spent much of his youth by his widow, Phoebe.

44

PRINCIPAL EVENTS OF LOCKE'S LIFE

1805   Joseph Locke born

1818   Apprenticed to William Stobart, agent and colliery viewer

1823   Apprenticed to George Stephenson

1825   Became Stephenson's paid assistant. Built Black Fell Colliery Railway for Stephenson.

1826   Began working for Stephenson on Liverpool & Manchester Railway

1829   Co-author with Robert Stephenson of pamphlet urging locomotive haulage on the Liverpool & Manchester Railway

1830   Drove *Rocket* at opening of Liverpool & Manchester Railway

1830   Became Member of Institution of Civil Engineers

1834   Married Phoebe McCreery

1835   Replaced George Stephenson as engineer of Grand Junction Railway (opened 1837)

1837   Began Glasgow, Paisley & Greenock Railway and Lancaster & Preston Junction Railway (both opened 1840)

1838   Became Fellow of the Royal Society. *Robert Stephenson's London & Birmingham Railway opened*

1839   Replaced Vignoles as engineer of Manchester & Sheffield Railway (opened 1845)

1840   Began building Crewe town and works

1841   Began Paris & Rouen Railway (opened 1843). *Brunel's Great Western Railway opened (Bristol-London)*

1842   Began Rouen & Le Havre Railway (opened 1847)

1844   Began Lancaster & Carlisle Railway and Colchester & Ipswich Railway

1845   Began Caledonian, Clydesdale Junction, Ipswich & Bury, Haughley & Norwich, Scottish Midland Junction, Scottish Central and Dutch Rhenish railways

1847   Became MP for Honiton. Lancaster & Carlisle Railway opened Caledonian Railway opened

1852   Began Mantes & Caen Railway (opened 1854)

1854   Began Caen & Cherbourg Railway (opened 1857)

1856   Dutch Rhenish Railway opened

1858   Became President of the Institution of Civil Engineers

1860   Died at Moffat

BIBLIOGRAPHY

Britain's First Trunk Line; N. W. Webster; Adams & Dart, 1972.

British Railway History 1830-76; Hamilton Ellis; Allen & Unwin, 1954. General account of early railway building.

The Caledonian Railway; O. S. Nock; Ian Allan, 1963.

Crewe to Carlisle; Brian Reed; Ian Allan, 1969.

Great Engineers; L. T. C. Rolt; Bell, 1962.

Joseph Locke — Railway Revolutionary; N. W. Webster; Allen & Unwin, 1970.

The Life of Joseph Locke; Joseph Devey; Bentley, 1862. Very rare and difficult to obtain.

Main Line over Shap; David A. W. Joy; Dalesman Publishing Co, 1967.

Master of Method; Charles Walker; David & Charles, 1975. A biography which examines Locke, his work and his methods.

The Railway Navvies; Terry Coleman; Hutchinson, 1965. Republished with revisions by Pelican Books, 1968.

Thomas Brassey — Railway Builder; Charles Walker; Muller, 1969.

INDEX

Page numbers in italic refer to illustrations.